SUPPORTING PRIMARY MATHEMATICS

WORKING with COLLEAGUES

Prepared by Joy Davis

Centre
for
Mathematics
Education

The Open
University

THE **SUPPORTING PRIMARY MATHEMATICS** TEAM

Joy Davis, Author and Chair

Alan Graham, Author

John Mason, Author

Gaynor Arrowsmith, Course Co-ordinator

Tracy Ellis, Secretary

Sue Glover, Publishing Editor

Ruth Hall, Graphic Designer

David Pimm, Academic Editor

Angela Walsh, External Assessor

ACKNOWLEDGEMENTS

We are most grateful to the following people who acted as critical readers for the project: Janet Ainley, Mary Briggs, Hilary Claire, Helen Gardner, Trevor Hart, Tim Howley, Wendy Nugent, Eleanor Oldham, Ian Sugarman and Nigel Williams. Any errors or omissions which remain in the pack are entirely the responsibility of the writing team.

We would also like to thank Lyndon Baker who took some of the photographs, and the pupils and teachers at the schools where photographs were taken.

Finally, we would like to thank our advisory team and higher education colleagues who attended the **Supporting Primary Mathematics** Conference, and all our colleagues at the Open University who have helped produce this pack so expediently.

The Open University, Walton Hall, Milton Keynes, MK7 6AA

First published 1990. Reprinted 1991.

Printed in Great Britain by Blackmore Press, Longmead, Shaftesbury, Dorset.

For further information on study packs and courses, write for a copy of *Open Opportunities* to Central Enquiry Service, PO Box 71, The Open University, Walton Hall, Milton Keynes MK7 6AG

ISBN 0 7492 4296 5

1.2

CONTENTS

ABOUT *SUPPORTING PRIMARY MATHEMATICS*

This booklet, *Working with colleagues*, is addressed to primary mathematics co-ordinators and to primary teachers who may not have such an official title, but who nevertheless find themselves providing a significant level of support for their colleagues' mathematical work in their school. We are assuming that readers have access to the other booklets in the pack, *Algebra*, *Shape and space*, *Probability* and *Handling data*.

This booklet aims:

- to support you in reviewing your co-ordinator role;

- to suggest some strategies for working on aspects of your role, and to bring to your notice other resources which might help you;

- to introduce you to the other booklets in this *SUPPORTING PRIMARY MATHEMATICS* pack, and to explain the intentions underlying them;

- to offer some ways of assisting you and your colleagues in working on the other booklets, and in working on mathematics together and with children.

In 1989, the Department of Education and Science offered funding for courses for primary mathematics co-ordinators. Part of the brief for such courses was the provision of support for co-ordinators to work with colleagues on the mathematics curriculum. This booklet forms one part of that support.

TEACHERS OF MATHEMATICS AND TEACHERS OF CHILDREN

It has been said that primary teachers see themselves as teachers of children, and not specifically as teachers of mathematics. Mathematics is just one part of the whole primary curriculum. Yet the mathematics National Curriculum draws teachers' attention to explicit lists of mathematical concepts that should be taught. However, mathematics does not just happen, and the more confident and mathematically aware you are, the better able you should be to make sensible choices and take advantage of mathematical opportunities when they arise.

The booklets in this pack are intended to help you to accommodate the mathematical demands of the National Curriculum in such a way as to fit comfortably with your self-image as teachers of children.

The way you listen and respond to pupils working mathematically, the way you intervene in the work of a group of pupils, the choices of activities you offer them, depend not only on your sensitivity to their individual, social and cultural needs, but also on what you see to be the mathematical potential that is present in a particular situation. Part of the task of a teacher is to recognise opportunities to make choices which will enrich pupils' experience, and promote their development on a wide front. Such opportunities may be fleeting. They occur in moments during classroom activity, moments when it is possible to say or do something which significantly affects what happens next, either for a group of pupils or for an individual.

The claim 'primary teachers are teachers of children' reflects a particular orientation in the choices that are made in these moments. It is the well-being of the children that takes priority. But there is usually little time to think about a range of options. If a pupil asks a question, when you approach a group immersed in some activity, you act and speak from your own reading of what it is best to do. This interpretation is bound up with your own experience, and with your beliefs, including all of your past mathematical experience and your range of beliefs about mathematics.

The four booklets about mathematical topics offer opportunities for you to refresh the mathematical experience from which you draw when you are planning lessons and choosing how to respond to situations which arise in your classroom. Each one contains an extensive range of activities for you to work on yourself and with colleagues. The activities may all be *adapted* for use with pupils, but they are presented in a style and form for *you* to work on.

It is our experience that it is through working on activities ourselves, at our own level, that we gain insight into the ways that they can best be presented to pupils, and into the ways in which we can best support their learning. Through working on your own mathematical thinking you may discover that fresh options are available to you in responding to pupils.

SUPPORTED SELF-STUDY

A group may form as part of an LEA or institution-based INSET course led by a member of the college staff or by advisory teachers. Alternatively, it may comprise all or some of the teachers within a school, guided by the mathematics co-ordinator, or someone nominated by the co-ordinator.

While there will certainly be individual teachers working on *SUPPORTING PRIMARY MATHEMATICS*, our intention is that the pack should be worked on in a supported self-study mode. The term 'supported self-study' describes the following way of working with material.

Before the end of the meeting, they all agree to read and work on a section chosen from the booklets.

Teachers sometimes meet to work together, with support from someone who is acting as leader for the group. Someone will prepare and present an activity chosen from a booklet or from another source, for the group to work on. After a period of work in pairs, and collective discussion, participants relate their experience to what they have noticed about their pupils.

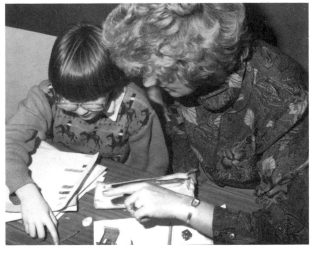

They also agree to modify some particular activities for use with pupils, and to report back their experience of using them with pupils at the next meeting.

ABOUT THE BOOKLETS

You will discover that two different styles have been used in writing the booklets, reflecting the different nature of the mathematical ideas involved. *Probability* and *Handling data* have a narrative style which requires that they are used starting at the beginning and working through them to the end. In contrast, *Algebra* and *Shape and space* have less of a narrative form. While their sections, initially at least, should be worked on in the order in which they occur, we suggest that you dip into the sections, picking out and exploring activities which attract you. To attempt all of the activities would either take a *very* long time, or would necessarily result in skimping and missing much of their potential.

Which booklet first?

We suggest that you begin by reading quickly through this booklet to get a feel for the ways in which it might be helpful to you. It can be used as a reference manual when particular issues arise, and as a source of ideas for meetings. We then recommend that you start with the first section of *Algebra* because the notion of *expressing generality* with which that booklet begins lies at the heart of all mathematics and so will inform the work that you do on the other booklets. Once you have got this under way, it would be appropriate to begin work on a second booklet, dipping back into the chapter Expressing generality from time to time. The booklets need not be worked on in any particular order.

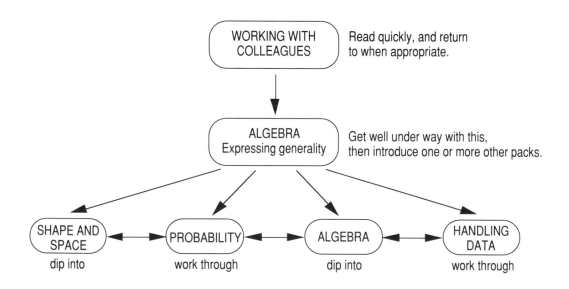

Here is an extract from *Probability*, as an example of the variety of types of writing you will find in any of the mathematical booklets.

CHANCE, ODDS AND PROBABILITY

The words 'chance', 'odds' and 'probability' are all ways of describing *uncertainty*. Considering what these three terms mean to you and how you think they differ. You may find it helpful to think about in what sort of situations you would use them.

The term 'odds' tends to be used within the domain of gambling and betting. There doesn't seem to be a clear distinction between the words 'chance' and 'probability', except that the term 'probability' tends to be used in more formal situations (like textbooks, for example). Differences emerge when we look at *how* uncertainty is measured – in particular, whether the measurement is based on use of *qualitative* descriptive words ('likely', 'improbable', 'certain', and so on) or on some sort of *quantitative* numerical scale (a 50% chance, a 1 in 10 chance, a probability of a third, and so on).

There are a great number of words which are used to describe chance. They cover a range from impossible, at one extreme, to certain, at the other.

Activities

There are lots and lots of these, so if you find that a particular activity does not attract you then either modify it, or move on!

Comments

Some of the activities are followed by comments written in smaller print.

Exposition

A certain amount of exposition links the activities together, so as to suggest a story underlying the choice of activities.

The activities

We cannot put everything into print that is pertinent to each activity. The things we have chosen to write should be regarded as springboards for your own classroom preparation as well as for exploration with colleagues. You may choose to work on an activity which is expressed in diagrammatic form by transforming it into one which uses Multilink cubes, attribute blocks, or some other favourite equipment. Or you may prefer to 'manipulate' the diagrams.

You will certainly want to modify the activities so as to phrase them in terms suitable for your children, drawing on appropriate equipment. Only you know the children you work with. The same activity, presented the same way, sometimes goes well and sometimes fizzles out. To try to suggest *all* the possibilities would be to write a very long book, so we leave it to you and your colleagues to think of ways of exploiting the activities we offer. A word of caution: beware of skipping through the booklets and not engaging with anything in particular. If you don't take part in activities, then nothing will happen.

Sometimes an activity will seem ambiguous, and you may feel reluctant to work on it without feeling you know what it means. We ask you to stay with the ambiguity. Our intention is that you should decide on your own interpretation and work consistently with that. The people who develop mathematics do so by making choices about meanings, and creating definitions from those choices. We work with their definitions when appropriate, so that we all mean the same thing by, say, 'circle'. One aspect of thinking mathematically is to encounter ambiguity, and to resolve it, so there will be opportunities of this type.

The comments

These rarely resemble anything that would be recognised as an 'answer'. Some make suggestions for modifying or extending the activity, some point out certain features of the activity. Most activities have been chosen because of the rich experiences that may emerge when you talk to colleagues about them. We have chosen not to recount our own experiences with the activities, since these might well block your own. Some programmes for INSET and staff meetings looks at some activities in detail, and at ways of using them.

Marginal notes

In *Algebra* and *Shape and space* you will find remarks in the margins containing thoughts that occurred to the writer, who felt they might prove interesting and stimulating.

CONFIDENCE

The word 'confidence' looms large in any review of the work of a co-ordinator: giving support to those who lack mathematical confidence; your own confidence as a teacher of mathematics; your confidence when working with colleagues.

Mary Briggs, who worked for six years as a primary mathematics co-ordinator in two very different LEAs, used her experience and range of contacts across her county to write a dissertation for an MA on the theme of teacher confidence, entitled *Perceptions of confidence*.

She sent a questionnaire to all the co-ordinators within a particular area, and followed it up with interviews with some of them. She doesn't claim that her work forms a complete account of confidence; there is certainly more to be found in other sources. But we have chosen to build this chapter on her work because she was looking at the issue through a mathematics co-ordinator's eyes.

CONFIDENCE IN MATHEMATICS

Mary Briggs believes that the lack of confidence which leads to a feeling of anxiety about mathematics does not come so much from the content of the subject, but rather from people's *experiences* in learning mathematics.

She supports this claim by reference to some of the research literature on mathematics anxiety, and goes on to discuss some of the experiences which can contribute to this lack of confidence. Among them, she cites:

- for women, gender issues, including the view that mathematics is a male domain; teacher expectations that boys will find it easy while girls are less likely to succeed;

- an emphasis on speed, with the associated (false) expectation that mathematicians find answers almost instantly;

- memories of failure.

(To explore gender issues with your colleagues in more detail, the Open University / ILEA pack, entitled *Girls into mathematics*, could provide a useful resource.)

PLAUSIBLE Does the claim that lack of confidence in mathematics comes from experiences gained while learning mathematics, rather than from the nature of the subject itself, seem plausible to you? When you cast your mind back over your own mathematical experience, what particular episodes first come into your mind? What do they tell you about *your* confidence with mathematics?

One central experience that abounds in mathematics, and that can sometimes rob us of confidence, is that of failure. One perspective, reflected in renewed interest in materials to extend able pupils, is that failure and challenge are *both* necessary to our development. Avoiding either can be stunting.

It is not the fact of failure, but the way in which it is handled and experienced, that is significant in our attitudes towards mathematics. It is likely that we have all had negative experiences with learning mathematics in the past.

This booklet adopts the notion that confidence in mathematics depends upon experience while learning mathematics, so opening the way for us to think about the kinds of experiences that help build pupils' confidence, and the kinds that hinder, while recognising that many situations are unlikely to be so clear cut.

In the chapter Working mathematically together there are suggestions for helping pupils to be confident with mathematics and for avoiding the negative effects of some experiences. The suggestions are of the kind that you can use yourself while working on the other booklets in the pack, while working with colleagues in school, and while working with pupils.

Here are some suggestions for looking at your own mathematical confidence, and at the way you respond to other people's confidence. (Be sure to write down some notes, or you may be left with only a vague sense of what happened.)

SOMETHING FOR YOU TO DO   In the coming weeks, make a note of the times when you feel that lack of confidence in mathematics is having a negative effect on your work as a teacher or colleague. Note down both what is causing the trouble, and how it affects you. Look for patterns.

Be alert to occasions when colleagues show lack of confidence. Make some notes about how you respond to them, and about the feelings that arise in you.

If you recognise that lack of mathematical confidence is an issue for you, then remember that you are not alone! There is a tendency to believe that others are much more confident and capable than ourselves, but once we have found the courage to admit to difficulties, then other people feel able to admit to doubts of their own.

There may also be an issue for you maintaining your role. Other co-ordinators and advisory teachers are among those who can be supportive.

SOMETHING TO DO WITH YOUR PUPILS
Note occasions in the classroom where a conversation with a pupil is affected by their lack of confidence. How did you recognise the confidence issue? How did you deal with it?

CONFIDENCE IN *TEACHING* MATHEMATICS

Mary Briggs defines confidence in mathematics teaching as *"feeling secure about the mathematical knowledge and skills which have to be taught, together with the ability to review one's practice, and to be able to take on board changes within one's own teaching situation"*.

Mary discovered claims in the research literature, such as the work by Barbara Fresko and David Ben-Chaim, that confidence in teaching and actual subject confidence are only partially interrelated. New entrants to the profession are often preoccupied with issues of classroom control and with discipline, while many experienced teachers may have their confidence undermined when they are expected to teach new topics or are required to use different teaching approaches.

No matter how expert we feel in any aspect of our activity, there is a point beyond which we feel uncertain. Problems arise in any teaching situation when, because of our own or other people's expectations, we are unable to admit that we don't know something, or that we are unable to do something.

Working in an atmosphere which is one of either knowing or not knowing, succeeding or failing, can result in feeling exposed and threatened. If you recognise this description, then one option open to you is to find ways by which you can change that atmosphere! Such a strategy would benefit both teachers and pupils with whom you work. The next chapter, Working mathematically together, offers suggestions as to how you might go about modifying the atmosphere in which you work.

REFLECTING Where does your confidence in teaching mathematics come from? Does it lie in your knowledge of the subject matter; in your repertoire of coping strategies; in detailed planning and preparation; or in . . .?

Commercial schemes of work were frequently mentioned to Mary by co-ordinators in relation to confidence in teaching mathematics. Here is what two of them said.

"People who would say they are confident in teaching mathematics are those who are

teaching page by page through the scheme. [. . .] They feel if they are following Fletcher then they are teaching mathematics."

"When I came here people definitely weren't confident. I talked to them individually and they were frightened by mathematics. With the scheme, their confidence has grown markedly."

These two statements by co-ordinators highlight two aspects of basing confidence in a scheme.

The second suggests that mathematical uncertainty can be countered by having good material which contains all the mathematics, and which is shared by other teachers in the school so that everyone is working to a commonly-agreed, explicitly-stated goal. The first, in contrast, points to one pitfall of a routine, unimaginative use of schemes. The final chapter in this booklet looks rather more closely at the implications of these co-ordinators' remarks.

SHARING

Being reminded about your role in supporting the confidence of others could be unnerving. All teachers go through periods of stress and change. You may feel you have enough to do in dealing with your *own* needs as a teacher.

Here is what some co-ordinators said about their *own* confidence.

"I'm not an expert and so I think it helps if I'm prepared to ask other teachers for suggestions. I want the staff to see the co-ordinator as someone who makes mistakes and can be seen coping with the day-to-day problems that everyone has."

"I also make a point of asking other members of staff for help if I am stuck."

A striking aspect of both of these remarks is that they are made by confident people. This is reflected in their readiness to admit to others when mistakes have been made, or that they have some difficulty which is proving hard to resolve.

The key to adopting the stance of these two co-ordinators lies in reflecting upon the image you hold of what it means to be a co-ordinator, and modifying that image if necessary. The affirmation *"I'm not an expert"* is one which permits you to acknowledge your own doubts and uncertainties and, occasionally, to turn to others for advice. In contrast, setting out to seem expert can be very isolating.

When circumstances force us to admit to a problem, it is remarkable how understanding and helpful others can be. More than that, other people begin to turn to us for help as well, and so a natural empathy develops. It is not your responsibility to know all the answers to mathematical issues in your school, but rather to be a colleague who can be turned to for a sympathetic ear and an opportunity to talk a problem through.

One key element in building confidence is the opportunity that exists for someone to exert influence. When such an opportunity arises for a teacher with whom you work, then that individual has a brief experience of leadership, of having their knowledge, skill or judgement appreciated and valued. It can be a rewarding experience for a teacher when their own good practice is recognised and adopted, suitably modified, by other teachers. You may choose to use the power of your position to enable others to experience this.

GOOD PRACTICE Can you identify a teacher in your own school whose practice could be of benefit to others and whose self-esteem would be enhanced?

What mechanisms might you use or have you used to discover such valued practice and to bring it to the notice of others?

What are the factors that hinder and help such strategies and how might you work with them?

Creating an atmosphere in which colleagues can comfortably and easily visit each other's classrooms is well worth working towards. There should be a total absence of judgement initially. Being observed teaching is so very threatening when we feel that someone is simply criticising what we do.

Begin by inviting a colleague to visit your own classroom after first making arrangements for the colleague's class to be taught by the headteacher (if a non-teaching head), or join two classes for some special activity. Be explicit that the purpose of working alongside you is not to judge or be judged, but to learn from each other. To avoid giving the message that your colleague is coming to learn from you, identify some particular aspect of the lesson that you would like the colleague to help you with, such as the way you get children started on activities, the way you bring them to a close, how you deal with a particularly unco-operative group or how resources are organised. Ask your colleague to make a few notes about things that they find striking, and make time to talk about these notes afterwards.

'Things that are striking' is a fairly neutral phrase. One teacher reported to another that she invariably ended a remark to pupils with *"OK?"*, a habit which hadn't been noticed before but which was then available to be worked on. She tried to become aware of being about to say *"OK?"*, and then to have an alternative phrase ready to use instead. She found that *"Is that alright?"* created a better opportunity for her pupils to reply *"not really"*, whereas *"OK?"* was proving harder to negate.

VISITING Find out from other co-ordinators, including co-ordinators of other subjects, whether they have tried to devise ways of getting people to visit each other's classrooms, and how they go about it.

There are many benefits to be obtained from establishing a habit of colleagues occasionally working together in the same classroom: opportunities for praising and disseminating good ideas, opportunities to seek help in handling particular children or particular parts of the curriculum, opportunities to notice that a colleague is in need of support. If you have not already done so, try beginning in a small way with yourself and one or two colleagues with whom you feel comfortable.

WORKING MATHEMATICALLY TOGETHER

This chapter describes a way of working on mathematical activities which puts a special emphasis on the creation of an atmosphere of trust and support within a group, whether of teachers or children. The notes are written with the following readers in mind:

- mathematics co-ordinators working together on a co-ordinators' course;

- advisory and college staff running such a course;

- co-ordinators wishing to work with other teachers on mathematics.

ESTABLISHING A CONJECTURING ATMOSPHERE

The following anecdote was related by a mathematics evening-class teacher. You may recognise similar experiences in your own learning, or in your work with children or as a co-ordinator.

"I'm finding one student, he's an engineer and about sixty years old, a bit difficult to deal with.

The problem is that every time I pose a question to the group, he answers immediately, in a loud and assertive voice. The result is that other students don't get an opportunity to answer, and the less confident ones lose more confidence through his all-knowingness.

I've tried beginning my questions with phrases like, 'Think about what I'm going to ask you quietly in your head for a few moments', but he seems not to hear and immediately bursts out with his answer. I cope with this by interrupting him with 'Quietly, to yourself, Ken!', but by then it's often too late, and he never seems to learn.

The other students are getting fed up with him, so I have to address the problem somehow. But I must also be careful not to damage his own confidence, since it takes a certain amount of courage to come to these evening classes, especially when most of the students are so much younger than he is."

Perhaps you are already rehearsing in your own mind strategies you have developed for coping with this kind of problem. The fact that so many people remain seemingly scarred by negative experiences of learning mathematics suggests that it would be helpful to be able to hear about the ways that other teachers go about developing a classroom atmosphere in which pupils can learn mathematics with confidence.

One way which has been found helpful by many teachers we would describe as *working in a conjecturing atmosphere*. We are not claiming that this is necessarily new or different to things you already do. It may be, though, that you are unused to establishing such an atmosphere among adults who bring with them their own mixed experiences of learning mathematics and who often need to be reminded of ways in which they can help themselves and others.

If Ken had been used to working in a conjecturing atmosphere, he would have developed the habit of sometimes holding back when an 'obvious' answer arose inside him so as to make space for others who are less sure. When making a contribution, he might couch it in terms like *"Perhaps . . ."* or *"I suggest that . . ."* which leave room for further discussion of other points of view.

Of course, there are always occasions when we feel excited by an insight, or experience an 'Aha!' and cannot help blurting this out, but if we behave like this all the time, then others will surely tire of such behaviour.

The most important aspect of helping others to feel confident about working on mathematical ideas together is to establish a positive, supportive environment. If everything that is said is taken as a conjecture, as an attempt by the speaker to clarify for themselves, with the intention of modifying and altering what is said if necessary, then everyone can participate in the inevitable struggles to learn. If, in responding to a question, everyone holds back until they are fairly sure that they have the right answer and can say it out loud, then there will be very little speaking, and even less discussion among members of the group. The confident members may blurt something out, and are likely to inhibit the others.

If the group leader focuses on the mathematical thinking that is going on, rather than on the answers, then participants can become aware of their innate ability to think mathematically, and confidence grows. By contrast, if attention is given primarily to judging the correctness of answers, which are expected to be right as often as possible, a few wrong answers can undermine confidence. If the group leader values and supports participants' struggles to express what they are thinking, they can afford to be wrong, because their speaking is an attempt to clarify and modify what they are thinking. Such an approach is needed right from the beginning of meetings.

To establish a conjecturing atmosphere, it is necessary first of all to feel that such an environment is important. Any group of co-ordinators or teachers working together on mathematics will inevitably span a broad spectrum of confidence and experience. It is the responsibility not only of the group leader, but of *everyone* , to be aware of the differing levels of confidence and to work supportively together.

One key belief is as follows:

> Those who have a lot of doubts and uncertainties inside them may have a lot more to offer other members of the group than those who feel knowledgable and confident.

To check this remark, try to recall occasions when you have felt a huge sense of relief when someone has made a contribution to a discussion or asked a question which has allowed you to examine your own understanding and modify it or otherwise develop it. In contrast, can you recall occasions when someone has made a firm, confident assertion which has moved the discussion on to other stages and left you with unresolved uncertainties and a sense of being left behind?

It is not so easy to speak up when we are uncertain. What is a conjecturing atmosphere, and how can you go about establishing one in your group?

As a participant in a group:

When you feel confident:
Listen to what others say.
Get them to clarify their thinking so you can understand.
Silently relate what they say to what you think.
Don't say *"No, that's wrong"*; rather, say something like *"Perhaps your suggestion needs modifying"*.
How do you listen? Don't interrupt others, or talk over them.
Avoid assertions which at one swoop tie up all ends – and leave some members of the group wondering where on earth the ideas came from.

When you are unsure or unclear:
Ask questions of whoever is speaking.
Ask for help and clarification, and try to say what you *do* understand.
Remember that if you are unsure of something, then there are almost certainly others in the group equally unsure. They will appreciate your efforts to express what you can.
Attend to how easy you are to be listened to. Speak loudly enough for others to hear. No matter how uncertain you feel inside, if you are able to begin with *"I suggest that . . ."* or *"Perhaps . . ."* then you are showing evidence of good mathematical thinking.

As a group leader you are asked to:

> Remind participants of what is meant by working as a group in a conjecturing atmosphere, especially when the *"No"*s start to come out.
>
> Value mathematical behaviour, such as conjecturing, by using remarks such as *"That's a nice example of mathematical thinking!"*
>
> Be consistent with these principles in your own behaviour. *Your* utterances should also have the status of conjectures.
>
> Be patient when what is expressed is confused.
>
> When someone says something, try asking others whether they have understood. If not, get them to question the speaker, rather than always acting as interpreter yourself.
>
> When discussing children and teaching, deflect judgements and concentrate on details which may enable others to recognise what is being described in terms of their own experience.
>
> Write down everyone's ideas on a board or flip chart. This helps each participant feel that their contribution is valued and gets their offerings outside themselves where they can be looked at more easily.

TRYING IT OUT

Questions and activities which are likely to generate more than one conjecture provide opportunities for a variety of creative contributions. This quality has been uppermost in our minds in choosing activities for the other booklets in this pack.

The best way to create and become familiar with a conjecturing atmosphere is to try to work in just such a way. Remember as you do so that the essence of this way of working is to create an environment which is supportive, and which, in particular, values expressing what you can see and what you know so far, rather than your ability to get things right, especially first time.

PUTTING IT INTO PRACTICE Below is an activity from *Shape and space.*

> **SQUIRREL** A dog spies a squirrel on a tree-stump. The dog runs round the stump in a circle barking furiously. The squirrel moves around on the stump, keeping to the side away from the dog so that the stump is between itself and the dog at all times. When the dog completes a circle, has it gone round the squirrel?

If you are a member of a group, work on it initially in twos or threes, and then discuss what you have been doing with the whole group. In both stages, try to reserve a portion of your attention for the *way* you are working, noticing the things that you do and say which support the development of a conjecturing atmosphere.

(If you are working by yourself, you can also be consistent with the suggestions that have been made by writing down your thoughts as conjectures, getting some informal words down on paper and then exploring around them.)

When you are satisfied that you have done enough work with the activity for the time being, talk together about what you noticed about the way you worked and the things that happened.

When a group of three primary teachers were offered SQUIRREL, one of them immediately responded with *"Of course!"*. The group leader noticed that the other two had been about to make a contribution but immediately stopped short, looking troubled. She read their expressions as indicating that they had been about to say something different, but they had now lost confidence and were unwilling to say anything much at all.

It was now left to the group leader to indicate that there might be more to the question than initially met the eye, and to open up discussion in such a way as to draw the other two in, indicating to them that they might have something of value to contribute. Once one of them had tentatively offered a reason as to why the dog might be regarded as *not* having gone round the squirrel, the first contributor's expression indicated that he now appreciated that *"Of course!"* had not been a helpful contribution.

The group leader chose to leave the particular discussion at the point at which everyone appreciated the need for care in defining terms.

The teachers left the meeting looking forward to seeing what their colleagues would make of it.

Of course, it may take some time and practice before you feel really confident about contributing and making suggestions when you are in a state of uncertainty. However, if you can only dip your toes into the water, you may well find it a positive experience that will make the next time so much easier.

CHILDREN 'GUESSING'

The notion of a conjecturing atmosphere is as relevant to your work with pupils as it is to working with fellow co-ordinators or with the teachers in your school. It is only the group leader that changes in the different contexts.

By creating a conjecturing atmosphere in your classroom, you may address some of the issues that arose in the previous chapter on confidence. Try the following activity with a group of co-ordinators or teachers.

CONJECTURING We suggested in the previous chapter that lack of confidence in mathematics stems from experiences while learning mathematics rather than from the nature of the subject itself.

How could you modify the notion of a conjecturing atmosphere for use in your own classroom, so as to foster the children's confidence in mathematics?

The word 'conjecture' might itself need some modification for use with pupils! The most suitable alternative is probably 'guessing', though some care is needed. It should be pointed out to them that their task is to make sensible guesses (at least some of the time) which build upon the evidence available from practical work and discussion. Of greater importance than the label 'conjecturing atmosphere' are the guidelines below which can be adapted for helping pupils to work supportively with each other and you.

Attainment Targets 1 and 9 of the mathematics National Curriculum are pervaded by the notion of conjecturing in the form of making predictions about what *will* happen if . . . A prediction is necessarily a conjecture based on the available evidence. As you work on the other booklets in this pack, be alert to activities which relate to these Attainment Targets. You should find plenty of food for thought, since the activities are largely open-ended and rich in opportunities for making conjectures or predictions, then testing and modifying them.

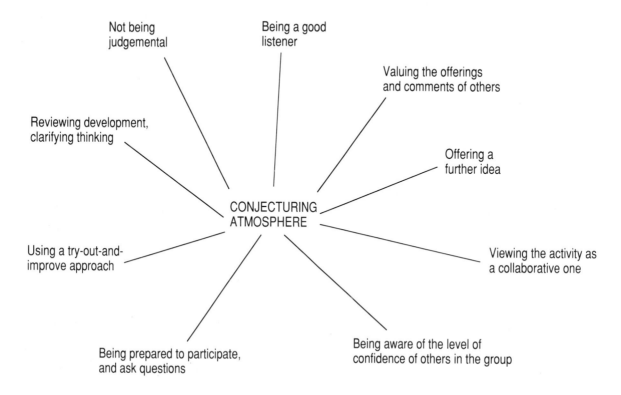

Not being judgemental

Being a good listener

Valuing the offerings and comments of others

Reviewing development, clarifying thinking

Offering a further idea

CONJECTURING ATMOSPHERE

Using a try-out-and-improve approach

Viewing the activity as a collaborative one

Being prepared to participate, and ask questions

Being aware of the level of confidence of others in the group

SOME TECHNIQUES FOR GROUP LEADERS

The following set of suggestions are appropriate for anyone leading a group of teachers or co-ordinators in working on their own mathematical thinking and on fostering the mathematical thinking of pupils. They are intended to take place within a conjecturing atmosphere.

Initiating activity

Get everyone to read the activity description. Sometimes, someone might helpfully volunteer to read it out loud to everyone else, because the tone of voice often shows up particular emphases being placed by the reader.

Ask participants to *"say what you see and think"* – perhaps to discover multiple interpretations.

Encourage people to suggest various different interpretations and approaches collectively and to outline one or more ways of getting started. Then ask each person or group to choose the approach that appeals to them most.

Sustaining activity

Vary the groupings – individuals, pairs, fours, . . .

Get participants (working in pairs) to describe to a colleague what has been done or where they are stuck.

Activities can be generalised and extended in different directions.

Outlining a conjecture provides a suitable place to pause or leave off work.

Explaining to someone else can clarify one's own thoughts and so can help to get going again.

Reflecting on activity

Point out that there is more to being mathematical than just doing the activity itself.

Ask participants to:

- recall salient moments, and to describe these briefly to a colleague;

- identify technical terms, as well as mathematical language patterns and images;

- construct a mathematical account of the activity.

Building on experience of using the activities with pupils

Use of brief but vivid anecdotes of classroom experiences, and a notebook, can help here.

Get participants to:

- look for similar experiences, resemblances and differences;

- discover different strategies that others use in similar situations.

Try to expose basic teaching tensions which may not be removable, but which can be coped with in different ways.

Watch out for *"Yes, but . . ."* as a response to a suggestion from a colleague (see page 37 for more on this).

In general, by selecting activities to work on and by focusing attention, a group leader can help people begin to work.

By drawing the group's attention to strong assertions of rightness or wrongness, a group leader can help establish a conjecturing atmosphere.

By sometimes responding to questions by asking someone else what they think, a group leader can demonstrate how the group could function without a leader.

By placing confidence in mathematical *thinking* rather than in mathematical knowledge, a group leader can demonstrate that even when you are stuck and don't know something, you can usually make some progress through first simplifying the problem, or trying some particularly simple cases. A sensible place to leave work on a problem is often with a clearly stated conjecture together, with a statement of any evidence available.

By valuing participants' contributions, even by simply acknowledging them as conjectures and inviting further consideration at another time, a group leader can help establish a collaborative, conjecturing atmosphere.

INTERLUDE: ON REFLECTION

The purpose of using mathematical activities is not only to carry them out, but to reflect on what you do so that you can build upon it some time in the future. The term 'reflection' is becoming a vogue word in education circles, but what does it consist of? Is it merely thinking back to some experience?

When you are in the midst of a situation which matters to you, you are having to make decisions and to react to what others do and say. There is often little time for thinking before acting. Your attention is likely to be focused on what is going on and your energy is probably flowing. In contrast, if someone asks you to reflect upon a lesson you taught last week, part of your attention may be on quite different things, and you may not be inclined to respond in anything but rather vague terms.

THINKING BACK Think back to last weekend. What do you recall?

It may be that in response to this invitation, you had to make some effort to drag yourself out of your reading mode, but that you were then able to recapture a flavour of your weekend: whether you stayed at home or went away, whether it was reasonably relaxed or rather hectic, . . . Your mind might have alighted on some specific events which occupied chunks of time within the weekend, such as visiting friends or shopping.

IMAGINING Now identify a short episode or incident in the weekend which stands out for you. Try to imagine yourself back in the incident so that you can feel vividly what it was like to be there.

A dictionary definition of 'reflection' offers *"to think, meditate or ponder"*. Next comes the definition that relates to mirrors: *"to form an image of something by reflection"*. The exercise above demonstrates how these two uses of reflection come together. *"Try to imagine yourself back . . ."* involves forming an image.

The image enables us to re-enter an event so as to experience it freshly. We may then recall in detail what we did, examine the effects of our decisions, and consider possible alternative courses of action. This is the essence of reflecting – to recognise the next time we are in a similar situation, *"Oh, I've been here before"*, and to be prepared to act or respond differently.

Recalling a weekend incident in detail may have attracted you, or it may have needed more effort than you felt willing to give. Reflection assumes some intention on your part, especially an intention to learn from your experience. It involves the senses, as well as the memory. Depending on your particular preferences, you may find yourself producing pictures, smells, sounds or feelings associated with an incident as part or all of your description.

SENSING Choose a moment from today which stands out vividly in your mind. Imagine yourself back in that moment. Which of your senses are involved in the imagining?

Now pick a moment from a recent lesson, and carry out the same exercise in relation to this moment.

Some people tend to focus on moments that they regret, others on their successes, or on 'nice things' that a child did or said in a lesson. Both are valuable; both may be enhanced if judgement is avoided. This requires letting go of desire to berate yourself, letting go of pride in what happened in your lesson.

PICTURING Try to picture or re-live the moment from a lesson that you just chose. Now try to describe it to a colleague.

Recalling moments from your teaching amounts to accumulating data which can provide a basis for effective communication with colleagues about teaching and learning. Here is a suggestion for an after-school meeting based on this idea.

TEACHING AND LEARNING Before the meeting, ask each of your colleagues to recall a moment or short episode from a recent lesson that stands out for them.

In the meeting, each participant recounts their moment in turn, keeping their account free from explanation or judgement. (The aim is to obtain a clean account *of* what happened, rather than to account *for* what took place.)

Then decide between you which account you will begin to work on. Choose one that many participants can recognise as common to their own experience. Work on the account by identifying the points within it at which the teacher made a decision. What decisions were made? What happened as a result of those particular decisions? What alternative decisions might have been made?

When you feel you have exhausted an account, move on to another.

In listening to the accounts of colleagues, each participant can be reminding themselves of what is significant for them, and thereby helping themselves to notice similar moments when they happen in the future. Through the discussion, you are also picking up suggestions for alternative responses that you could use in the future.

Working with other co-ordinators in this way could help you in your co-ordinating role; with fellow teachers, it can help you in the classroom.

TAKING STOCK

Although there is a long tradition of posts of responsibility for primary mathematics, the role of the mathematics co-ordinator was first described in detail in the 1982 Cockcroft report, *Mathematics counts*, and indeed this report employs one of the first systematic uses of the term 'co-ordinator'.

It suggested that, *"The effectiveness of the mathematics teaching in a primary school can be considerably enhanced if one teacher is given responsibility for the planning, co-ordination and oversight of work in mathematics throughout the school."* (The original range of duties recommended by the Cockcroft Committee is given on the next page, though it was composed during a quite different educational era to the present one of the National Curriculum.)

Recent surveys have confirmed that few co-ordinators undertake all of these tasks. In fact, there is enormous variation from county to county, from school to school. Marion Stow and Derek Foxman, in their book *Mathematics coordination*, describe the various roles which the co-ordinators they spoke with were fulfilling during the period 1985 – 1987.

THE ROLE OF A CO-ORDINATOR

It is beyond the scope of this booklet to look in detail at all aspects of the role of co-ordinator. However, the recent book *Mathematics in ILEA primary schools* offers a useful enhanced overview of the way in which the role might develop over time, and identifies three stages in this development: *getting started as a new co-ordinator*, *moving on*, and *continuing work as an established co-ordinator*, giving descriptions of typical co-ordinator activity in each stage.

Although this booklet is not specifically about organisational issues, it does offer you an opportunity to look at the ways in which your role has developed over time, and why it has taken those particular directions. Such a review might also assist you in negotiating changes which will help you and your colleagues adjust to current developments in education.

If you are a headteacher with responsibility for mathematics in your school, we hope you will find food for thought in these pages. Many have found, for example, that the benefits of greater freedom of choice from being a head are offset by interference from their status as head. It may be hard to adopt a conjecturing atmosphere if all look to you for policy.

The Cockcroft report

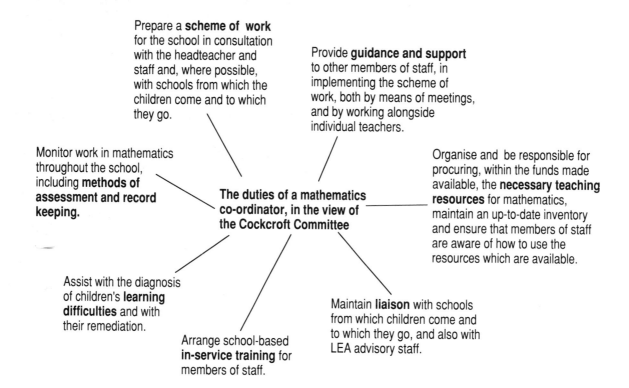

Prepare a **scheme of work** for the school in consultation with the headteacher and staff and, where possible, with schools from which the children come and to which they go.

Provide **guidance and support** to other members of staff, in implementing the scheme of work, both by means of meetings, and by working alongside individual teachers.

Monitor work in mathematics throughout the school, including **methods of assessment and record keeping.**

Organise and be responsible for procuring, within the funds made available, the **necessary teaching resources** for mathematics, maintain an up-to-date inventory and ensure that members of staff are aware of how to use the resources which are available.

The duties of a mathematics co-ordinator, in the view of the Cockcroft Committee

Assist with the diagnosis of children's **learning difficulties** and with their remediation.

Maintain **liaison** with schools from which children come and to which they go, and also with LEA advisory staff.

Arrange school-based **in-service training** for members of staff.

The Cockcroft report claims that the over-riding task must be to provide support for all who teach mathematics, particularly probationary teachers, teachers new to the staff and those who lack confidence in teaching mathematics.

The report lists, as the needs of the co-ordinator:

- good support from the headteacher;
- appropriate in-service education;
- some modification of aspects of the co-ordinator's timetable in order to make it possible to work alongside other teachers.

NATIONAL CURRICULUM The Cockcroft report was compiled long before the advent of the mathematics National Curriculum. In consultation with a group of co-ordinators, or perhaps with your own colleagues, consider the ways in which the range of suggested duties needs to be modified to take account of the existence of the mathematics National Curriculum.

WHAT DO YOU DO? What are the various tasks that you perform as co-ordinator?

For each of your responsibilities, recall to mind some instance in which you have carried it out, and if you are working in a group, describe it to them without judgement or elaboration.

In the light of the Cockcroft report, and of your response to the activity NATIONAL CURRICULUM, are there any items which you would like to add to your own responsibilities, or which you feel need otherwise to be attended to in your school?

Which responsibilities are you comfortable with and believe you accomplish reasonably well and which are you not fully at ease with?

Although we are unlikely to address all these facets of your work in this booklet, you may well come across references to other sources of assistance.

Do you have a job description for your co-ordinating responsibilities? If so, how does it compare with your response to WHAT DO YOU DO? If not, discussion of your work with this booklet with your headteacher might provide a means of negotiating a job description. Working instinctively rather than from a job description is fine when everyone shares the same image of what needs to happen, but you could be rather vulnerable without one if ideas differ – as they have a habit of doing.

SOME FACTORS THAT HELP, AND THOSE THAT HINDER

In WHAT DO YOU DO?, you were asked to try to identify particular tasks which you feel you do well, and those where you are less content about what you are able to do.

DRAINING AND GAINING Choose one of the tasks and think back to a specific occasion when you were attempting to carry out that task. Recall it as vividly as you can, trying to re-experience what it was like. What was it that enhanced your effectiveness, and what drained your confidence?

In everything we do, we are more at ease with some facets of the experience than with others. We tend to seek out the former and avoid the latter, if we can. Discomfort arises in our work when we are unable to avoid unwelcome tasks, or when we avoid them and let other people down. Discomfort, though, is one of the jolts that can knock us out of mere adequacy and can stimulate us to undertake a review of what is happening, with the intention of making some changes, however small. When things are comfortable, there is little impetus for change. The work of Edward de Bono (see page 58) provides strategies for changing behaviour, by altering customary modes of thinking.

The table below suggests a way of looking at a situation with the intention of identifying and working on the particular aspects that help you and those that hinder you.

Factors that hinder	Actions to reduce the factors that hinder
Factors that help	Actions to harness the factors that help

For example, the obstacles which hinder arranging meetings with colleagues to work on this pack can be so strong as to be disheartening! They may include the reluctance of some colleagues to find the time, the pressure of other agenda items or your own lack of confidence in leading such meetings.

Actions which co-ordinators have taken to reduce these obstacles include:

* initially meeting only with those teachers who wish to be involved: other teachers became attracted to joining in by overhearing accounts of what was going on;

* limiting the discussion of administrative concerns to the first (or last) fifteen minutes of a meeting, or arranging for staff meetings to deal alternately with business and teaching concerns;

* asking a colleague to lead meetings.

Helping factors in arranging meetings may include a supportive headteacher, ideas in this booklet, or an imminent school INSET day.

HELPING YOURSELF What helping factors could you draw on to arrange meetings with your fellow teachers to work on *SUPPORTING PRIMARY MATHEMATICS*, or to address issues of teaching and learning more generally?

How could you increase and exploit those factors? What about your obstacles?

Colleagues who are willing to prompt you to home in on what helps and what hinders you can be of real assistance. In particular, probing the obstacles may reveal an element of avoidance of actually getting meetings underway.

When you confront a table like the one on page 30, or a questionnaire, there is a risk of only scratching the surface, of writing things down rather mechanically without making any real contact with the issues concerned. In contrast, when you are feeling sufficiently discomfited in your work to say to yourself, *"I really must do something about this!"*, then that is the time to sit down and analyse the factors of both kinds that are present in the situation.

The power of the method of analysing helping and hindering factors is that it encourages you to approach a problem from two directions at once, and to identify actions that are within your power to undertake. It does not suggest that you can eliminate or ignore the obstacles, but rather that you can possibly reduce their effects. The possibility of harnessing the helping factors to increase their effects is one which is often overlooked when tackling a problem, since there is a marked tendency to concentrate exclusively on difficulties.

When you have used the table once or twice, it is possible that the notion of helping and hindering factors will come into your mind in the midst of activity, and be available for you to notice and to work on there and then.

For example, when finding it difficult to come to an agreement with your colleagues about some new mathematics materials for the school, you might realise that you have overlooked the helping factor that is the availability of an advisory teacher with detailed knowledge of a whole range of schemes. You might cast your mind over possible hindering factors which are preventing progress and realise that you have omitted to try to agree about the strengths and weaknesses of your existing scheme, so that people are carrying with them a variety of mixed feelings about the need for change.

WORKSHOP IDEAS

Here are suggestions for two workshops which together could form a day's INSET activity for a group of co-ordinators, or an INSET day for a school's teaching staff, or two after-school meetings (provided that these are held on consecutive weeks).

Each participant is asked to identify a concern with which they would like to make progress, and to work on it with the help of other participants. Examples of the kinds of concerns that might arise in a co-ordinators' workshop are:

- how can I influence a colleague to be more open, more exploratory?

- we need a new mathematics scheme and I'm not sure what is available or how to choose between them;

- I'd like to do more to improve communication with parents and to make more of the help they might be able to give. How can I start?

And for school-based meetings:

- I'm having real trouble with a few parents who think we're not doing enough proper mathematics;

- although the children are chatting a lot when they're doing their mathematics, I'm not sure that what they're doing is 'discussion';

- some remarks a teacher friend made to me the other day made me think that we're lagging behind in the liaison we're doing with our secondary schools.

The aim of the meeting is to draw up an action plan for each concern. The workshops make use of the concepts of helping and hindering factors. Since they invite participants to be open about concerns, it is important that an atmosphere of trust is established from the start. You may have your own preferred ways of going about this.

We suggest you:

- give enough time for people to introduce each other, and learn names;

- begin with a short exercise in which participants say what they most enjoy about their work;

- try to work with the group in a conjecturing atmosphere;

- most particularly, take care not to be judgemental, and discourage only judgemental remarks from others – especially when people judge themselves, saying things like: *"I know I'm stupid, but . . ."*, *"This is probably wrong, but . . ."*.

The structure of our suggested meetings is as follows.

Workshop 1 Generating alternatives

Brainstorm concerns and note ideas.

(i) *Getting started*: work in groups of four to six people, or as near to this as possible.

(ii) In each group, decide which of you will initially act as 'concern bringer' (they bring their concerns to the group for consultation among colleagues). The others will act as 'resource' (you will eventually change roles). Concern bringers should choose a concern with which they genuinely need help.

(iii) *Briefing (5 minutes)*: Concern bringers give a short description of their concern to their group, including the following information:

- how it affects them personally;
- what they have tried and/or thought of so far;
- what sorts of things they have the power to do;
- what they would most like to be able to do.

While being briefed, the rest of the group should:

- listen carefully;
- make notes of *anything* that occurs to them (whether or not it seems immediately relevant);
- resist the temptation to ask questions;
- make sure the concern bringer covers all points listed above.

(iv) *Brainstorming (10 minutes)*: the rest of the group should now use the notes made during the briefing to work on the problem. During this brainstorming phase, the concern bringer should listen for new ideas, and where appropriate, feed in their own (keeping a note of all ideas generated).

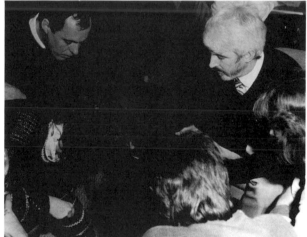

The following brainstorming guidelines might be of assistance.

- Suspend judgement
  Do not judge or evaluate the ideas being offered, whether they are yours or other people's. Laugh *with* wild ideas, not at them.

- Quantity
  Go for sheer quantity of ideas, not quality. Quality implies evaluation, which is better avoided at this stage.
- Cross-fertilise
  Be prepared to pick up someone else's idea and suggest others leading from it.

(v) Now change roles and repeat the briefing and brainstorming steps with a new concern offered by a different participant.

(vi) Retain your notes of the ideas generated, for use later on.

Interval

Between workshops, concern bringers should work on the notes they have taken, by using them to draw up an *action plan*, bearing in mind how the ideas brainstormed relate to the factors that help and those that hinder them.

An *action plan* requires some detail in order that it can be acted upon, for example timings and names will be needed against various parts of it.

Workshop 2 Putting the plan into action

In this workshop you will discuss action plans and suggest strategies for their implementation, and again act both as concern bringer and as resource.

(i) Split into the same groups as before, and decide whose concern and action plan will be worked on first.

(ii) Concern bringers describe to their groups their preferred action plan, pointing out the main helping and hindering factors.

(iii) The groups then ask questions of the concern bringer about the action plan, paying particular attention to:

- how the hindering factors can be reduced or immobilised;
- how the helping factors may be mobilised;
- any tendency by the concern bringer to respond to suggestions with *"Yes, but . . ."*

(iv) Change roles and repeat the presentation and brainstorming, looking at the action plan of another concern bringer.

Naturally, it would be nice if a group were able to meet about a month later, to hear how action plans are going, and to provide more help and support. If this is not possible, then before you leave the second workshop, pair up and agree to try to support each other within your pairs, perhaps through an occasional telephone call.

INTERLUDE: POWER AND CONTROL

The word 'power' may seem strange, perhaps discomfiting, to meet in relation to primary schools. Power has been described as the ability to get other people to behave in the way you want them to, an ability which it would surely be useful to have sometimes. Working with people who have power is not the same as working with those who wield it unfairly and in large amounts. Having power does not sit comfortably with many people, yet your co-ordinator status will inevitably carry a certain amount of power with it – although it may not seem that way to you. In fact, specific mention was made of the power of your position on page 15 in connection with encouraging colleagues to visit each other's classrooms.

This interlude looks at different kinds of power with a view to helping you to recognise its presence and understand it, and thereby to use it constructively. It draws on an analysis of power proposed by Charles Handy in *Understanding organisations*.

We look at three different aspects: position power, resource power, and negative power. Our invitation is to use Handy's analysis to look at the kinds of power that you can recognise as being available and/or at work in your school.

Position power is readily recognised as the power that accompanies positions of responsibility of different kinds, from caretaker to headteacher – and including co-ordinator. Stories abound of ways in which it can be wielded negatively. For example, those who are keepers of keys can make it unreasonably difficult for others to have access to certain rooms or equipment. Sometimes those with the *smallest* positions contrive to wield the most power over others!

POWER-FULL With other co-ordinators, if possible, identify the areas of power that you have by virtue of your co-ordinating position. For example, you may identify the power to call meetings and to decide on their agendas, or the power to decide how to spend your capitation budget.

Which powers are you most able to exercise by consultation, and which do you find yourself exercising alone?

One of the most effective ways of ensuring that you are not seen by colleagues as exercising your position power unreasonably is to check that you are not only *listening* to colleagues when they make suggestions, but actively *consulting* them and seeking their help.

Naturally, headteachers have the most position power. Marion Stow, in *Managing mathematics in the primary school*, identifies five types of headteacher, each characterised by certain attitudes, and suggests strategies for working with them.

She calls her five: 'non-supportive', 'nominally supportive', 'indecisive', 'dictation not delegation', and 'fully supportive'. Their characterising attitudes vary from *"You have the post – get on with it"*, to *"Let's talk and listen. Everyone counts"*.

Among her suggestions to co-ordinators for working with headteachers is the following.

> *"Ask for an annual meeting with the headteacher, to set out broad policy targets for co-ordination. Prior to the meeting, give some thought to your ideas based on what you think is needed and what you consider to be achievable. Write down your ideas."*

Resource power is such a significant kind of position power that it warrants special examination. It involves both the possession and the control of resources and probably comprises the greatest proportion of the power you have by virtue of your position. Since the way you use this power affects everybody in the school, and so inevitably affects your relationship with each of your colleagues, consultation and co-operation over managing resources are essential.

Discussion about resources can take up a lot of staff meeting time, not always profitably. Devising a system of ordering, maintaining and organising resources which everyone understands and supports is clearly desirable, since it is so easy to create dissent by seeming to use your resource power unfairly. What seems perfectly fair and well organised to you may be perceived as unreasonable and haphazard to someone else.

CONSULTING Invite your colleagues to each write down two suggestions which might improve the organisation of mathematics resources in your school.

What do their suggestions tell you about resource issues in your school? If you find yourself working with a group of co-ordinators, take the suggestions that you have received from your own colleagues and compare them with those made to the other co-ordinators. How does what they have in common inform you about resource issues?

The feedback you obtain would probably provide a good starting point for workshops to devise an action plan on resources, as outlined earlier in the previous chapter, Taking stock.

Much has been written about managing resources in all the books about the co-ordination of mathematics. Marion Stow looks at resources under the headings 'organisation', 'implementation' and 'utilisation', while the ILEA document

Mathematics in ILEA primary schools specifically considers 'apparatus', 'calculators' and 'computer software'.

Negative power is power that is used to block ideas and actions. It is present in utterances which begin *"Yes, but..."*, an all-too-familiar response to any suggestion that is made.

YES, AND (For group work) Split up into pairs to undertake the following role play activity.

Imagine you are two people chatting to each other in a bus queue. Person *A* gets the conversation going, while person *B* tries their best to respond to everything that *A* says with *"Yes, but . . ."*. For example: *A* says *"Isn't it a lovely day!"*, to which *B* responds with *"Yes, but it isn't going to last"*. After four minutes, swop roles.

Next, go through the exercise again, but this time you respond to everything that is said with *"Yes, and . . ."*.

What did you notice? Join with other pairs to pool experiences.

Of course, responding to everything with a *"Yes, but"* or with a *"Yes, and"* is going over the top, but it can provide a stark reminder of how easy it is to adopt a blocking stance, and how much more difficult but more positive it is to be open to *"Yes, and . . ."*.

CHANGING RESPONSES Set yourself to notice the occasions when you respond to some suggestion that a colleague makes with *"Yes, but . . ."*. Next time you feel that response coming up inside you, try changing it to *"Yes, and . . ."*.

Catching yourself on the point of saying it (or something equivalent) is not easy; at first, you are likely to notice the *"Yes, but"* after it has already slipped out, but you will get better with practice. Of course, countering the negative reactions of others is even harder. Being receptive yourself to the ideas of others is a good starting point. If you can generate a positive atmosphere, then others might be influenced by your attitude.

Negative power is not universally a bad thing; there are times when it is useful and even necessary to be able to block. The point of the activity YES, AND is to draw attention to the ease with which we slip into a negative mode, often without being aware that this has happened. Consequently, we may sometimes use this power unreasonably.

The three types of power looked at here do not, of course, comprise the whole range of power that you will meet in your work. Try to become attuned to the presence of power in its various forms – including charisma (personal power), traditional power (*"I've been here for twenty years and . . ."*), and hierarchical power (by virtue of the authority structure in school, both formal and informal).

If you recognise that a particular difficulty you are encountering can be ascribed to the way that someone is wielding some sort of power, then you have a starting point from which to tackle the problem. It may be that you will need the help of your headteacher in redefining or clarifying structures so as to modify someone's position or hierarchical power, or of another co-ordinator or advisory teacher, if that is more appropriate (i.e. harnessing the helping factors). Contending with issues of power is part of being a co-ordinator.

SOME CURRICULUM ISSUES

This chapter looks briefly at two school areas which have major implications for the work of a mathematics co-ordinator: commercial schemes, and theme or topic work.

COMMERCIAL WORK SCHEMES

Some of the activities in this section will be appropriate only to co-ordinators whose schools use schemes. Others may use the remarks made in this section to review the alternatives which have been developed in their schools.

Schemes were mentioned briefly on page 14 in connection with confidence in teaching mathematics. There we suggested that schemes, like so many things that we find useful, have their disadvantages as well as their advantages. They bring with them the benefits of supporting teachers' confidence in knowing what to teach and how to teach it. They can be used to provide some consistency throughout the school. On the other hand, they can be used unimaginatively and routinely.

A 1989 HMI report on the teaching and learning of mathematics in primary schools, entitled *Aspects of primary education*, highlights two particular dangers in relying on commercial schemes exclusively.

- Insufficient time given to direct teaching and discussion in order to consolidate the children's grasp of important mathematical principles and to allow their findings and difficulties to be discussed.

- Too much practice of skills that have already been mastered, so that children may be bored, and for the most able the work is often too easy.

These problems were first highlighted in an HMI report in 1978, and HMI found that they have worsened significantly in the last decade.

CONSULTING Obtain a copy of the 1989 HMI report from your headteacher or mathematics adviser and use it as the basis of a meeting or more informal consultation with your colleagues about the relationship between HMI's findings and their own views about the commercial schemes they use (if any).

HMI reported that:

> *"The most effective materials had been devised by teachers themselves, guided by a consistent policy agreed by the whole staff: in other schools, the absence of agreed guidelines and common policies resulted in work lacking progression, pace and challenge."*

GOOD PRACTICE What kinds of good practice with respect to the use of learning resources (whether texts, work schemes or original material) are you aware of in your school?

GOOD AND BAD What do you gain as a school, and as an individual teacher, from using a commercial scheme?

HMI's criticism of the way commercial schemes are used mention their *exclusive* use. This is the key issue: not that they are used, but that they may constitute children's *total* experience of learning mathematics.

For teachers to devise their own materials is clearly a desirable but hugely time-consuming task. An alternative, middle path consists of ways of *augmenting* your scheme. For example, you may decide that the scheme you use is not adequate in the way it deals with a particular common misconception, or that it is unlikely to help children develop the appropriate mental imagery connected with a particular topic.

The other booklets in this pack offer a myriad of activities which, suitably modified, can be used to augment your own resources. While working on the activities, bear in mind the experiences which your own resources provide for pupils, and keep a note of the ideas that come to you for augmenting those materials.

Exploit your mathematics advisory service, and the curriculum and teachers' centres they run, for advice about choosing commercial schemes and for opportunities to browse through the examples they have collected.

THEME AND TOPIC WORK

A teacher describing approaches to primary mathematics recently said, *"Well, there's the schemes, and there's theme and topic work"*. In drawing attention to the value of exploratory work in motivating pupils to produce good mathematics, HMI also reported:

> *"A lot of interesting and worthwhile mathematics arose from carefully chosen cross-curricular themes and topics."*

THEME PLANNING With other co ordinators or with your own colleagues, examine the process of planning and implementing theme work in your school. How much co-ordination is there between teachers?

As with commercial schemes, theme work has its pitfalls. For example:

- it can be the case that pupils only encounter the same rather trivial areas of mathematics in their theme work;

- unless care is taken in whole-school planning, children may work on the same themes again and again as they progress through the school, but without any mathematical progression being visible.

An extensive exploration of the topic *food* forms the basis of an extremely constructive booklet, entitled *The National Curriculum – making it work for the primary school*, produced jointly by the Association for Science Education, the Association of Teachers of Mathematics, the Mathematical Association and the National Association for the Teaching of English. The topic work is carefully planned, with grids indicating how the work relates to the whole curriculum and to Profile Components and Attainment Targets for the core curriculum subjects. Three activities are developed in detail: investigating jelly, survey of what we ate yesterday, and investigating the shape and pattern of cut fruit. Finally, a grid is suggested for seeing what opportunities each activity offered for meeting the statements of attainment at Levels 1–3.

The writers admit that the kind of analysis described in the booklet took them a long time to do, but they also expect that with practice this would become much more a part of their routine, and would take less time.

The ILEA handbook (which we mentioned earlier) points out that there is not always a tidy link between a cross-curricular topic and particular concepts. It supports the view given in the subject associations' booklet by emphasising that a procedure is needed for analysing topics to ensure that they build properly on children's previous experiences and existing skills, and to ensure that certain curriculum items are not ignored.

It may be that this rather brief survey of two such major aspects of primary mathematics teaching will have stimulated some questioning in your mind about current practice in your school. They form ideal territory for working on concerns in workshops, as described in the chapter Taking stock.

We have chosen, in this booklet, to pay a lot of attention to the notion of working mathematically with colleagues, rather than to look in detail at the whole range of organisational issues with which you have to deal. The reason for this choice is that we want to help you to work effectively and with pleasure with the other booklets in the pack. However, the resources to which we have referred throughout the booklet offer assistance with issues which we have not been able to include, such as writing or modifying a whole-school mathematics plan, multicultural issues or the role of assessment.

We hope, especially, that the booklets in this pack prove of assistance to you in your mathematics teaching, and also provide you with many stimulating hours.

SOME PROGRAMMES FOR INSET AND STAFF MEETINGS

Our aim is to provide you with a starting point for your work on the booklets with your own colleagues. The programmes exemplify the variety of activities available, and ways in which they can be used, so that your colleagues can become familiar with the style and content of the four booklets. Of course, each booklet contains much more than there is room to include here, and you will find in each one a carefully-structured development which can only be hinted at in the programmes.

What is their format?

The programmes may be used in any order, and consist of extracts from the four 'content' booklets in this pack, set in a framework of Activities, Talking points and Reflections. Most sessions begin with a particular extract from the booklets which sets the scene and might help you stimulate discussion.

Each programme is structured in three 'sessions' designed for whole-day INSET or staff meetings and comprising a pre-coffee session, a pre-lunch session and an afternoon session. You could, instead, use each programme for a series of three after-school staff meetings. If you do this, then agree to undertake some work with children based on what has happened during the meeting, and report back at the next meeting.

Naturally, nothing in the programmes is irrevocably fixed. You might prefer to change the activities for others in the booklets, or for some of your own.

What do I need to do before using one of the programmes?

*   Remind yourself of the content of Working mathematically together, and of Interlude: on reflection in this booklet. You may find the final section of the chapter, Working mathematically together, entitled *Techniques for group leaders*, particularly pertinent.

*   Make the practical arrangements for the meeting, consulting your colleagues beforehand about which programme they would prefer to work on.

*   Check whether the chosen programme has any particular equipment requirements. This will be stated at the start.

*   Ensure that sufficient copies of *Mathematics in the National Curriculum* are available for consultation.

ALGEBRA

Whatever impressions of algebra you currently have, we want to convince you that a very large part of the mathematics taught to pupils is really about seeing patterns, interpreting what is seen, and expressing those patterns in words and symbols. The important patterns are the ones which are not just particular to one situation, but which apply to many different but similar situations and are therefore generalisations. Expressing those perceived generalities *is* the root of algebra.

(You will need some Lego or other bricks for the second session.)

First session Expressing generality

Children seem to enjoy games with words, perhaps because the means of expression become objects to play with.

Begin by working together on the following word game.

WORD CHAINS For each of the following chains, add at least two more words which extend a pattern you see.

cereal, bowl, glass, window, . . .

big, bright, red, small, . . .

big, bright, beautiful, blue, . . .

dog, growl, light, tap, pop, page, . . .

Now working in pairs, exchange your chains with your partner's and try to extend your partner's chains even further, by detecting the pattern your partner has seen.

TALKING POINT Much of mathematics teaching is about encouraging children to become more articulate about the patterns they find, and to be able to use them in their thinking.

How might you modify WORD CHAINS to work with children in such a way as to encourage them to become more articulate about the patterns they find? How would you organise you classroom for this work?

Number chains provide a source of similar activities. AT5 Level 3 states:

"Explain number patterns and predict subsequent numbers where appropriate."

WHERE TO NEXT? Extend each of the following sequences in at least two different ways, and each time try to describe your rule in words.

1, 2, 3, . . .
2, 4, 6, . . .
1, 3, 5, . . .

For example, 2, 4, 6 might continue 2, 4, 6, 2, 4, 6, over and over which arises when checking groups of eggs laid out in half-dozens. Note the use of '. . .' to indicate something which can be carried on indefinitely.

Now try to produce rules for these chains, and make some for colleagues to try.

1, 2, 4, 5, 7, 8, 10, 11, . . .
1, 4, 5, 9, 14, . . .

1, 3, 2, 7, 6, 11, . . .
1, 3, 7, 13, . . .

1, 2, 3, 2, 3, 4, 3, 4, 5, . . .
6, 23, 2, 1, 4, 5, . . .

REFLECTION What stands out for you from what you have done so far? Has your work with these activities reminded you of similar experiences you have had with children?

Second session Approaching algebra

BRICK WALL Decide how you are going to continue the picture sequence.

The best way to do this is to make or draw some more yourself, and then say what you are doing in words: that is the first expression of generality.

Once you have specified a way of extending the sequence of pictures indefinitely using a rule, there is a unique answer to counting the number of bricks needed to make any particular wall (such as the 37th one, which is a typical middling-sized number). There are usually many different ways of seeing *how* to do the counting, which therefore gives rein to creativity.

Sometimes it is easier to draw a picture to *show* how you are counting, rather than to say it in words. For example, here are two of the many different ways of seeing the Lego brick sequence. Notice that the pictures have become two-dimensional because they are easier to draw.

"I see one brick, with none, then with one, then with two, . . . pairs of bricks added on."

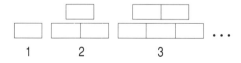

"I see two rows, the top row having one brick less than the bottom row. The bottom row has one, two, three, . . . bricks in it, depending on its sequence position."

45

Each of the different ways of seeing gives rise to a way of counting, which can be expressed more succinctly (as your confidence grows), until it looks very much like a formula. Thus:

> Picture number 37 will have two rows of bricks. There will be 37 bricks in the bottom row, and 36 bricks in the top row.

This can, when appropriate, be shortened to:

> Picture 37 needs 37 (bottom row) + 36 (top row) bricks.

Algebraic thinking has already begun. By the time facility has been achieved in being able to find the number of bricks needed in particular cases, sufficient attention is freed to deal with a question which promotes seeing and expressing generality.

HOW MANY BRICKS? I have a picture-number in my head. Tell me how to calculate how many bricks that picture has.

This question takes us into the heart of algebra seen as expressing generality. It is taken up in detail in the chapter A route to algebra. Work together to express how many bricks are needed.

Picture sequences with something worth counting can come from many sources such as children's own drawings or using traditional designs from different cultures, and they can arise spontaneously at unexpected moments. For example, while producing a Christmas picture, children in one class were drawing trees. They soon realised they could make bigger and bigger versions, and that they could count the twigs, or the twig-ends, not just for particular trees, but for any such tree no matter how large.

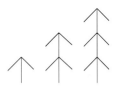

Third session Patterns in arithmetic

Children can encounter the as-yet-unknown in the creative aspects of arithmetic.

After observing that you can do

$$4 + 6 =$$

turn it around and ask

$$10 = ? + ?$$

There are all sorts of possibilities for the first '?', rather fewer for the second once the first has been chosen. This provides direct experience of the idea of an unknown or variable.

CREATIVE ARITHMETIC Find numbers which fit the following 'un-arithmetic' statements, paying attention to the amount of freedom you have left after filling in each box.

$$12 = \square + \square$$
$$12 = \square - \square$$
$$12 = \square \times \square$$
$$12 = \square \div \square$$

$$12 = \square + \square - \square \ldots$$
$$12 = \square \square \square$$

What makes the freedom different in different instances?

TALKING POINT Most schemes ask children to fill in the box in questions like $3 + \square = 7$. Once children work out how to do them, they seem to lose touch with the original purpose, which is to experience the complementarity between addition and subtraction, and to get a sense of finding an unknown number. For most, it becomes just another kind of question with another kind of technique.

What are the features of CREATIVE ARITHMETIC which might counter this observed loss of contact with the challenge of working with the unknown?

AUGMENTING How would you use CREATIVE ARITHMETIC to modify or augment your work scheme or texts?

NATIONAL CURRICULUM Choose one statement from the mathematics National Curriculum which you and your colleagues agree to be essentially concerned with pre-algebra and devise an activity which gives pupils the opportunity to see and express patterns or generality.

How would you organise your classroom in order to work with your activity?

REFLECTION What moments stand out for you from your experiences today? Try to re-enter those moments in your mind, as sharply as possible.

Draw up a plan of how you might continue working together on pre-algebra after today. What do you wish to work on and how do you wish to structure your way of working?

SHAPE AND SPACE

We live and move in a three-dimensional world full of shapes, we draw and write about them in a two-dimensional world, we see television and cinema screens as looking through a window.

(For the first session, you will need a collection of solid shapes – two copies of each. They might be made up from Multilink cubes, or come from a set of prisms and pyramids: they might be packages, etc. You will also need identical collections of cards on each of which is drawn a shape. (See RECOGNISING 2-D SHAPES below.) Be sure to provide a set of cards for each pair of participants.)

First session Working with shape

RECOGNISING 3-D SHAPES Display one copy of each object, and place the second copy of one of them in a bag or *Feely box* (so that others can see). Now get someone to feel the object and describe what features they are using to identify which it is.

This is an example of becoming aware of what you are stressing in order to identify something.

TALKING POINT When you are identifying an object, you are not only stressing certain of its features, you are also ignoring others which are not relevant to the task. When asked to engage in some activity, children often stress and ignore rather different features from those you had in mind! For example, they may stress colour, when you had intended them to concentrate on shape.

Spend a few minutes recalling and exchanging examples of this sort from your own teaching. How do you respond to the children when they misinterpret your intentions?

While working on the next activity, try to notice the roles that stressing and ignoring play in what you do.

RECOGNISING 2-D SHAPES Make up a collection of shapes, or a pack of cards with shape drawings like those shown below, and sort them into groups. Provide a name for each group. Then look at how other people have sorted them, and try to work out the basis of their sorting, providing names for their groups. Then compare notes.

TALKING POINT Children are often asked to carry out this sort of activity, but often it is implied that there is a unique name for a given shape. Rarely in mathematics is this the case!

"An 'oblong' is a rectangle, but not all rectangles are oblongs (some are squares), and rectangles are also parallelograms."

Discuss these assertions, with the aim of agreeing to some drawings of:

- a rectangle that is an oblong, and one that is not;
- a rectangle that is also a parallelogram, and a parallelogram that is not a rectangle.

Second session Imagining

The vital seeds of geometrical thinking, which are sown in the early years of formal schooling are concerned largely with establishing flexible and confident movement from the physical world of action to the mental world of image and thought, and back again.

In this session, try to work entirely with your own mental images, avoiding both pencil and paper and drawing in space with hands and arms.

ONE CUT Imagine a straight line drawn across a square, and a cut along that line. What shapes can the pieces be? How many different ways can it be done?

What shapes could you make from multiple copies of one or other, or both of the pieces?

The number of different ways will depend on how you classify the shapes arising from the cutting. You can actually cut squares up, but you can also draw the lines and imagine them cut. You can even look at a sketch of a square and mentally move the line around to determine what shapes you get.

The next activity has also to do with cutting. The interesting part of it lies in describing your cut to someone else so that they too can see what you are seeing. What matters most is paying attention to how you get better at describing, not so much to the actual shape of the cuts!

SECTIONS OF A CUBE Imagine a cube. It may help to have a large one beside you. Now imagine that a sharp knife cuts through in a single slice. What shape do you see when you look at where the cut was made (called the *section*)? For example, can the section be a square? A rectangle? A triangle? What other shapes can there be? What kinds of triangles can you achieve? What kinds of rectangles?

TALKING POINT In both ONE CUT and SECTIONS OF A CUBE, if you resort to cutting paper, or marking a cube, you make it easier, but you may lose contact with exercising your descriptive powers.

Think ahead to activities you will be using shortly with children. Can you identify one or two which could be used as exercises in mental imagery? What would be the advantages and disadvantages of using the activities in this way?

Third session Measuring – forays into angle and area

The word 'geometry' originally referred to the measurement of the Earth ('geo' meaning "Earth" and 'metry' meaning "measurement"). It soon came to mean much more, however. Early geometers were concerned about very practical matters such as measuring plots of ground for tax purposes, and how to locate property boundaries after flooding. Their investigations led them to study properties of lines, circles and other curves.

The idea of angle is embedded in our language, and words and phrases connected with angle are used frequently in and out of the classroom.

IMAGINING This activity invites you to create some mental images. It is therefore helpful if someone reads the following instructions out loud. Children might like to act them out.

"Close your eyes. Imagine a short straight line segment (a piece of a straight line). Make it move around a little and then bring it to rest in the middle of your field of vision. Bring in another line segment and move it around until their ends meet. Think of where they meet as a hinge; open and close the hinge. Get used to opening and closing the hinge, to get a sense of angle. Arrange it so that you have a very small angle between the two lines. Now make the angle between the two lines very large. Try making angles of approximately 60°, 120°, 180°, 270°, 360°, 420°."

TALKING POINT Discuss in pairs what you experienced. Draw some pictures if it helps. Write down some of the words and phrases to do with angle that were used in your discussion and compare notes with others. Bear in mind the statement of AT10, Level 4:

"understand and use language associated with angle".

An awareness of the language patterns associated with angle is a good starting point when preparing to teach the topic.

To measure areas, you need to approximate the region by a collection of rectangles or squares. The difficulty is actually the same in both cases: you can only measure as accurately as the units with which you are measuring. Whereas length and angle have beginnings and ends, so you start measuring at zero and finish at your measurement, areas (and volumes) only have boundaries, and this makes them seem different.

CARVE UP In fraction work, children are often invited to divide a region up, shade in some of the parts, and then announce what fraction of the whole has been shaded. What fraction of the whole has been shaded in each of the following? Make up your own examples.

TALKING POINT In pairs, describe to your partner how you saw the diagrams in CARVE UP. What did you stress and what did you ignore?

Shadows are part of every child's experience. Why can you not stand on your shadow's head?

> *"You'd have to get there before you moved."*
> *"You'd have to get there in no time at all."*
> *"You'd have to move faster than light."*

What fun it is to stand on someone else's shadow's head!

There are some important mathematical ideas which derive from the notion of shadows, including trigonometry, the roots of which lie in the early years of school. For example, if you see a shadow, how much can you reconstruct about the object?

SHADOWS Here are some drawings of shadows. What might they be shadows of?

TALKING POINT In what sense do shadows measure things?

REFLECTION The mathematics National Curriculum AT10 Level 3 states:
> *"Sort 2-D and 3-D shapes in different ways and give reasons for each method of sorting."*

Think back over your experiences today, and try to identify moments which provide insight into the skills and understanding required by this Attainment Target.

PROBABILITY

(This programme requires some work to be done by teachers before the day.)

One justification for reflecting on, and learning about, probability is to become better at making decisions. Most, if not all, real-life decisions involve *uncertainty* – indeed, you could argue that a decision without uncertainty present is no decision at all.

SOMETHING TO DO BEFOREHAND Be on the look-out over the next few days for occasions when you hear words or phrases associated with uncertainty or probability. Make a note of as many examples as you are able and bring them to the meeting.

First session Talking about chance

COMPARING NOTES Working first in pairs, and then in larger groups, compare the examples of the use of the language of uncertainty and probability that you have brought with you.

What do these tell you about the experience of uncertainty and ideas about probability that your pupils bring with them to the classroom? What other knowledge and experience might your pupils have that you can draw on in your teaching?

A fruitful area for discussion is to engage children in conversations which explore their understanding of words like 'definite', 'possible', 'probable', and so on.

DEFINITE? In pairs, write down lots of future events on cards and then place each card on one of three piles – 'definite', 'possible' and 'definitely not'. Attend to the factors which emerge in your negotiations with your partner about which pile to place events in.

Then, in the whole group, discuss what has emerged for you out of this activity.

TALKING POINT What do you think are the strengths and weaknesses of DEFINITE? as an activity for use with pupils? What modifications, if any, would you make?

NATIONAL CURRICULUM AT14 Levels 1 and 2 are about the notion that certain events may produce a variety of different outcomes.

Drawing on the work you have just been doing, about the language of chance and probability, how might you help young children to be more aware of this idea?

Second session Measuring chance

As is clear from the first session, there are a great number of words which are used to describe chance. They cover a range from impossible, at one extreme, to certain, at the other.

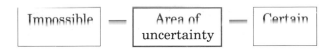

| Impossible | — | Area of uncertainty | — | Certain |

Numerical probabilities arise from thinking of this range of descriptions in terms of a number line from 0 to 1.

Here are a number of phrases commonly used to describe the chance of an event happening.

A   Almost certain

B   Not in a month of Sundays

C   An even chance

D   Beyond all reasonable doubt

E   Possible

F   Probable

WEIGHING UP THE CHANCES Using the six letters A to F, mark on the number line above where you think each of these phrases should be placed.

Compare your results with a colleague and see if you agree.

Think up some more 'chance phrases' (for example, 'very likely', 'highly improbable', 'more than likely', and so on) and see if you can agree where they should be placed on the number line.

Mathematicians try to tie down, to quantify uncertainty by expressing a probability of some outcome happening as a number between 0 and 1. For example, suppose that there are ten balls in a bag, three of which are white and seven red.

BALLS IN A BAG Suppose you shake the bag and pull out a ball, without seeing it. What is the chance that the ball is white?

Intuitively, most people would agree that, because there are 10 balls altogether, and only 3 of them are white, you have 3 chances in 10 to pick a white ball.

Contrast this approach to BALLS IN A BAG with the following extract from a conversation with Carrie (aged 7). (A stands for adult.)

A   Imagine I have a bag here with three white balls and seven red balls. Got that?

C   Yeah.

A   I put my hand in and pull a ball out. OK? You don't know what it is. What do you think it might be?

C   A red ball.

A   Why do you say that?

C   'Cos there's more red balls than white balls . . . and there's more chance of you pulling out a red ball than a white ball.

A   Why is there more chance of pulling out a red ball?

C   Well, there's only three white balls and there are seven red balls. Um. The red balls will cover more of the space, 'cos there's seven of them. And if there's only three white balls, it'd be a bit weird if you pulled out a white ball.

These aspects of probability will be returned to in the third session.

Third session Probability and the mathematics National Curriculum

In the second session, Carrie remarked that there is more of a chance of pulling a red ball out of the bag because *"The red balls will cover more of the space"*. In BALLS IN A BAG, this chance was (implicitly) quantified as $\frac{7}{10}$, contrasted with $\frac{3}{10}$ for a white ball.

NATIONAL CURRICULUM Look at the statements of attainment from Level 1 to Level 5 of Attainment Target 14, the probability area of handling data.

Work together on the *progression* from Level 1 to Level 5 by relating the statements of attainment to your experience of working on the activities in the first and second sessions. Try to identify the way in which the statements chart the transition from Carrie's *intuitive* understanding of chance, to the *quantifying* of chance.

Pay particular attention to the role of the language of probability in the statements of attainment. Which aspects of the Attainment Targets are well supported by your existing resources, and where are there gaps?

REFLECTION Think back over your work with these probability activities. What stands out for you that you think will be of significance in your teaching of AT 14 (*"Pupils should understand, estimate and calculate probabilities."*)?

PLANNING As a group, decide what you would like to do next, in relation to teaching probability. For example, you might agree to engage your pupils in conversation about chance, perhaps through the medium of a story, and then meet together to report what happened before agreeing a next stage.

HANDLING DATA

(This programme requires some work to be done by teachers before the day. See SOMETHING TO DO BEFOREHAND on page 57.)

It is actually very hard to handle data *to a purpose* unless you know why the data were collected in the first place. There must have been an initial question which provided the impetus to collect the data. You will find that it is this initial question which is used as the main criterion for sorting out all the other stages in the data-handling process.

(You will need a tiny packet of raisins – obtainable in supermarkets – for each participant, and a packet of *Post-it* labels of the type used to record messages.)

First session Posing questions

Where are the various questions which are to form the basis of classroom investigations to come from?

REFLECTION Think back to recent work that you have carried out with your class in curriculum areas other than mathematics.

(a) What sorts of questions were the pupils asking and responding to?

(b) What opportunities were there for purposeful handling of data resulting from these or similar questions?

(c) What role, if any, was there for calculators and a computer?

One teacher recorded the following example.

I asked the children to bring in lots of different leaves from home and school. We tried hard to identify them (not very successfully!). A book from the school library proved to be very helpful in putting names to them. I told the children we were going to play 'tree detectives', but first they needed to find a way of recognising the leaves. We looked at things like colour, size, shape, feel, edge, and so on. Each leaf was measured and classified and all the data were entered onto a computer database. It took quite a long time to enter all the data, but when it was complete, I invited them to write down a question each that they thought the database might help us answer. Some of their questions could be answered directly from the database. For example:
"What trees have the biggest leaves?"
However, other questions, such as:
"How many leaves are there on each tree?"
couldn't!
But some of the latter type of question sparked off interest in further investigations. We went on to press some of the leaves to make a leaf scrapbook and one group made leaf tiles out of clay.

TALKING POINT Bearing in mind your response to REFLECTION, as well as the teacher's response above, find some *particular* issues for your group to work on involving cross-curriculum work and data handling. For example:

- developing the use of databases (the chapter Collecting data in the booklet *Probability* offers some suggestions);

- taking some particular examples of the theme work offered to your pupils, and examining them for opportunities for handling data.

TALKING POINT What sorts of issues are the children you teach particularly interested in (pets, sport, environment, TV, pop music, local issues, . . .)? What sources are there where you might find interesting data on some of these issues (e.g. *TV* and *Radio Times*, local paper, TV, comics, *Smash Hits*)?

Second session Collecting data

Among the methods of data collection considered in the booklet *Handling data* are surveys and questionnaires. Both involve choosing a sample population to survey or question. If you wish to select a *random sample*, you must ensure that each item from the whole population has an equal chance of being selected.

SAMPLING BIAS Below are examples of sampling. Discuss with a colleague some possible sources of sampling bias.

(i) Using a telephone survey to predict national voting intentions in the general election.

(ii) Conducting a weekday street poll to survey attitudes on capital punishment.

(iii) Carrying out a traffic survey at 8:00 a.m. every morning for 10 days to assess pedestrian safety.

(iv) The headteacher makes decisions on the school's response to the mathematics National Curriculum on the basis of a meeting with the board of governors.

TALKING POINT What do you feel to be the key notions underlying sampling? How might you help very young children begin to think about some of these ideas? Here is one teacher's response to these questions.

"For my infants, the most likely place where sampling might crop up is when we do some cooking. Sometimes when we make fudge, we put a few drops of the mixture into cold water every so often to see if it is ready to set. I might ask them questions like 'How many drops should we use?' and 'Why not use more / less than that?' This should help them to think about why we bother to take samples at all and the idea that we can tell something about the whole panful by just testing a few drops."

Can you think of examples from your own teaching which you could exploit to help children with the notion of sampling?

By the time they reach the final stages of primary school, most children are already familiar with seeing numerical information represented in tables, block graphs (both bar charts and histograms) and pie charts. Some may even have used scatter graphs but, for reasons of space, these are not covered in the *Handling data* booklet.

But what about infant pupils? Can they have direct access to graphical representations, and, if so, what is the best way to introduce them? Concrete (physical) embodiments are usually the best starting points for young children, and graphs are no exception.

TALKING POINT Read through Levels 1 and 2 of AT13. Try to devise suitable classroom activities which will help young children to use and interpret block graphs and Carroll diagrams.

Third session An investigation

Each participant should be supplied with a tiny pack of raisins and four *Post-it* labels.

SOMETHING TO DO BEFOREHAND Each participant asks four friends to estimate the number of raisins in the packet, to write the estimate – without divulging it – on a *Post-it* label and to place the label in an envelope.

To begin the session, each participant is asked to write their own raisin estimate on a label, without divulging it to others.

TALKING POINT How did members of the group come to their estimates?

Collect together all the estimates (including those collected beforehand) and stick the labels on the wall so as to form a block graph.

TALKING POINT Pooling ideas, how many statements can you make about the graph? (For example, you might consider such features as maximum, minimum, spread, average, . . .)

HOW MANY? It's time to open the packets and count the raisins. How will you represent the data? How will you count accurately so everyone will agree?

It would be nice to be able to compare the actual figures with the estimates. How do you take account of the fact that five estimates were made for each box?

TALKING POINT What opportunities for your work with children can be discovered in your own experience with the raisin boxes?

REFLECTION Before leaving, take a few moments to recall a moment or moments in your work with *Handling data* which seem of particular significance to you.

REFERENCES AND RESOURCES

TEXT REFERENCES AND FURTHER RESOURCES

George Ball *et al.*, 1990, *Talking and learning: primary mathematics for the National Curriculum*, Blackwell.

Mary Briggs, 1989, *Perceptions of confidence: an investigation into primary mathematics co-ordinators' perceptions of their colleagues' confidence in teaching mathematics*, unpublished dissertation, MA in Curriculum Studies, University of London Institute of Education.

Edward de Bono, 1971, *The use of lateral thinking*, Penguin.

Edward de Bono, 1972, *Children solve problems*, Penguin.

Edward de Bono, 1973, *Po– beyond yes and no*, Pelican.

Charles Desforges and Anne Cockburn, 1987, *Understanding the mathematics teacher: a study of practice in first schools*, Falmer Press.

Barbara Fresko and David Ben-Chaim, 1986, 'Competence, confidence and in-service education for mathematics teachers', *Journal of Education for Teaching*, **12** (3), pp.285–294.

Charles Handy, 1981, *Understanding organisations*, Penguin.

HMI, 1989, *Aspects of primary education – the teaching and learning of mathematics*, Department of Education and Science.

Jennifer Nias, 1989, Primary teachers talking – a study of teaching as work, Routledge.

Marion Stow, 1989, *Managing mathematics in the primary school: a practical resource for the co-ordinator*, NFER-Nelson.

Marion Stow with Derek Foxman, 1988, *Mathematics coordination: a study of practice in primary and middle schools*, NFER-Nelson.

Mike Sullivan (ed.), 1990, *Supporting change in primary schools*, Blackwell.

David Winteridge (ed.), 1989, *A handbook for primary mathematics co-ordinators*, Paul Chapman Publishing Ltd.

Girls into mathematics, 1986, PM645, The Open University in association with The Inner London Education Authority, Cambridge University Press.

INSET material for Programmes of Study in mathematics, to appear autumn 1990, National Curriculum Council.

Mathematics counts – the report of the Cockcroft Committee, 1982, HMSO.

Mathematics in ILEA primary schools: making it happen. Part 2. A handbook for the mathematics co-ordinator, 1988. Available from Centre for Learning Resources, 275 Kennington Lane, London SE11 5QZ.

The national curriculum – making it work for the primary school, 1989, prepared by the Association for Science Education, the Association for Teachers of Mathematics, the Mathematical Association and the National Association for the Teaching of English. Published by Association for Science Education.